Through the Rainbow

Indigo Book 1

All through the Day

by E. S. BRADBURNE
Illustrated by LESLEY BELLAMY

SCHOFIELD & SIMS LTD., HUDDERSFIELD

Simon and Elizabeth are going to school.
Simon is putting on his coat and hat.
Do up your coat, says mummy.
Come here
and let me help you to do it up.
I can do it myself, says Simon.
Let me do it.
I will do it up myself.

Elizabeth is putting on her coat and hat.
Can you do up your coat, Elizabeth?
says mummy,
or would you like me to help you?
Can you do it up by yourself?
Come here and let me help you.
I can do it, says Elizabeth.
I can do it all by myself.
Let me do it myself.
Look at me, I can do it.

Have you got your book, Simon?
says mummy.
And has Elizabeth got her book
and her pencil?
Have you got your pencil, Simon?
Here are some apples for you to eat
at school.
Off you go.

Simon and Elizabeth go to school by bus.
You must go and catch the bus,
says mummy.
Off you go. You will have to run.
Goodbye, she says.
Goodbye Simon, goodbye Elizabeth.
Goodbye mummy, says Simon.
Goodbye, says Elizabeth.
Come on, Elizabeth, says Simon.
Follow me, run. Run fast.

All the children in the street
go in the bus.
They go to school by bus every day.
It is a big bus, with 6 wheels.
Every day they see it
coming up the street
to take them to school.
It is waiting at the end of the street
for Simon and Elizabeth.
Come on Elizabeth, says Simon.
The bus is waiting.
Come on, run! Follow me.

My pencil, says Elizabeth,
I have not got it.
It is on the table at home.
I will go back for it, says Simon.
I will fetch your pencil for you.
I can run fast.
Simon is running back home to fetch
Elizabeth's pencil.
The bus is waiting for him.
It is waiting at the end of the street.
Hurry up! says Elizabeth.
Hurry up! Simon.
Run! run fast!

Did you get it? says Elizabeth.
Did you get my pencil?
Here it is, says Simon.
I have got it for you.
I did run fast to fetch it.
Come on Elizabeth, hurry.
We must run to catch the bus.
Follow me.
We must run fast.

I can see the bus waiting for us,
says Simon.
All the children are on it,
and the driver is waiting to go.
We will miss it, says Elizabeth,
hurry Simon.
We must hurry
when the bus is waiting for us.
Come on Simon, run.
The driver can see Simon and Elizabeth.
He is waiting for them to catch up.
They are getting in.
We did not miss it, says Elizabeth.
We did not miss it after all.
Everybody is in the bus and it can go.
The driver is making the engine go.
The wheels are going round.
They are going round fast.
I like it going fast, says Simon.
And I like it going fast, says Elizabeth.

Simon and Elizabeth
are at the front of the bus.
I like being at the front, says Simon.
I can see when I am at the front.
Simon is by the window.
He can see out.
Elizabeth is next to him.
I would like to be by the window
and see out,
says Elizabeth, let me have a turn.
It is my turn, says Simon.
It is my turn to be by the window first.
You can be by the window after.
You can have your turn next.
You can have your turn when we come home.
Have you got the apples? says Elizabeth.
What did you do with them?
I would like to eat them.
When can we eat them, Simon?
We must not eat them in the bus,
says Simon.
They are for us to eat at school.

Some of the children
are on the top of the bus.
They are on the top deck.
They like going up there.
They can see all round
when they are on the top deck.
Look, says one of the children,
I can see someone
in the garden down there,
and there is a dog in the next garden
and a cat up a tree.
I can see a train over there.
I like being on the top deck.

The bus is going down the street.
It is going up the next street
and down the next.
It is going all round the houses
to fetch the children
to take them to school.
All the people in the houses
look at the bus going by,
taking the children to school.
They can see the bus going fast.
They can see Simon and Elizabeth
at the front.
They can see Simon by the window.
They can see the driver
at the front of the bus.
They can see the children on the top deck.
They can see the bus
going round the houses.
They see the bus every day.

Now the bus has come to the school.
Here we are, says Simon,
here we are at school.
Now we must get off.
Simon and Elizabeth get off the bus first
and all the children follow them.
Come on, says Simon, follow me.
Have you got your book and pencil,
Elizabeth? he says.
Have you got the apples? says Elizabeth.
Come on into school, says Simon.
Hurry up.
The children are taking off their clothes.
Simon is taking off his coat.
Take off your coat and hat, Elizabeth,
he says.
Put them up here by my coat.
Put your clothes here.
Elizabeth is taking off her coat and hat.
She is putting them
by the side of Simon's.

Now the children are in school.
They are making a house
with the bricks.
They have made a window in the house.
They are making a tower in the sand.
Some of them are playing
in the play house.
Elizabeth is making a man out of clay.
Look at my man, she says.
I made him myself.
Simon is making an aeroplane out of wood.
Look at my aeroplane, he says.
I made it myself.
Come here, says the teacher,
come round me here.
Tell me what you did with the clay
and the sand.
Tell me what you did with the wood
and the bricks.
Tell me what you did in the play house.
Let me see what you have made.

Can you draw a picture of what you did,
and write about it? says the teacher.
Fetch your books and I will help you.
I would like to see what you did.
When you have finished
you can come and read
to me, she says.
Fetch your books and read them to me.
You are good children, says the teacher.
It is my turn to read first,
says Elizabeth.
Can I read to you now?
I can read all my book, I have finished it.
Elizabeth is going to read her book
to the teacher.

The children are singing.
They are singing about a little tree
in a magic wood.
Do you like singing? says Elizabeth, I do.
I like singing to my doll in bed.
I like singing when I am up a tree,
says Simon.
I like singing to myself.

Daddy is going to work.
He has to go every day.
He has to go by train.
Let me help you to put on your coat,
says mummy.
Have you got your hat? she says.
You must hurry
or you will miss your train.
Goodbye, says mummy.
Goodbye, says daddy.
Goodbye, baby, says daddy, be good.

Daddy has to go to the station
to catch his train.
The station is at the end of the street.
Here is the train coming now!
The signal is down
and the train is coming fast.
Daddy can see it coming.
My train! says daddy.
He must run fast or he will miss it.

The train is not waiting for him.
It is going fast.
It is going out of the station.
All the people have got on the train
and daddy is not on it.
Goodbye, goodbye, says the train.
Daddy is waiting for the next one.

Mummy has to work in the house.
She has to tidy up
after the children go to school.
She has to make the bed
and wash and dry the dishes.
She has to wash the clothes
and put them out to dry.
She has to dust the house
and mend the socks.
She has to make the dinner for baby.
She has to take Spot out and give him
his dinner.

Mummy is going to put the clothes out
in the garden to dry.
They will get dry in the garden,
says mummy.
Now she has to make a cake for tea.
She has to cook every day.
She has to mop and dust.
She has to mop and dust
all round the house
and she has to make the fire.
Spot has got the mop.
He is running away with it.
He is making a big dust with it.
The dust is going all over the clothes.
Naughty Spot!
Give me the mop, says mummy.
Put it down, naughty Spot!
Give me the mop, put it down here.

When she has finished the work
in the house
mummy has to go to the shops.
She has to go to the shops every day.
The shops are at the end of the street.
She is going to buy some buns
and some jam for tea.
Simon and Elizabeth like jam.
She is going to take the baby with her
to the shops.
Spot would like to go to the shops
with mummy and baby.
He is not to go with them.
Mummy is not going to let him come.
Go to your bed, says mummy.
Go back to your bed, Spot.
Go to your bed by the fire.
Be a good dog.
You must not come with us.
You must not follow us to the shops.

Mummy is going out now.
Spot does not go to his bed.
He is going out in the garden.
He is playing with the clothes.
He has got all the clothes down
on the grass.
Naughty Spot!
Now mummy will have to wash them
and put them by the fire to dry.
I will have to make up a big fire
to get the clothes dry, says mummy,
naughty Spot!

Now school is over.
The children have finished their work.
They have finished reading their books.
Here they are coming home for their tea.
They are coming back in the bus.
Simon and Elizabeth are on the top deck.
Let me be by the window now,
says Elizabeth.
It is my turn. It is my turn to see out.
I like being by the window, she says.
I like being at the front of the bus.
I like to look out.
What can you see, Simon?
I like being on the top deck.
I can see the people in their houses.
Look, there is a fire engine
coming down the street. It is going fast.
All the people are coming out to see it.
I am hungry, says Simon.
Are you hungry, Elizabeth?
Will there be jam for tea? says Simon.
I like jam. I would like my tea now.

Daddy has finished his work.
Now he is coming home.
He is coming home for his tea.
He is coming back in the fast train.
He is by the window.
He did not miss the train coming back.
Mummy will be making the tea for him.
She will have the kettle on.
He will be hungry for his tea.

Mummy has made the fire.
The clothes are all dry.
She has made a big fire.
I must put the kettle on for tea,
she says.
Daddy is coming in.
Is the kettle on? he says.
Have you made the tea for us?
Is there some jam for tea?
I am hungry.
Can I help you to get the tea?
The kettle is singing, says mummy.
I will make the tea now.
Did you miss your train? says mummy.
Tell me all about it.

The children have come home from school.
They are hungry.
They are going to have tea.
There are some buns for tea.
I am hungry, says Simon.
Can we eat the buns now?
I am hungry, says Elizabeth.
Is there some jam for tea?
I would like some jam.
Can we have jam on the buns?
What about the cake? says daddy.
I would like some of the cake you made,
mummy.
Is there some cake? says Simon.
Is it for us?
Did you make it, mummy? says Elizabeth.
This is good cake, says daddy.
I like it.

Tell me about school, says mummy.
Tell me all about it.
What did you do?
I can read, says Simon.
I can read all my book
and I can write.
I can read, says Elizabeth,
and I can write.
I can write a story.
Look, this is my story.
I made this book for you.

Now I will help you to wash up,
says daddy.
I will dry the dishes.
Give me the mop, says daddy.
I am good at this.
I will help you to dry the dishes,
says Simon.
And I will put them away,
says Elizabeth.
Now all the work is finished
and they are all by the fire.
Tell us a story, mummy, says Simon.
Tell us a story now.
I will read you a story, says mummy.
What story would you like?
Read us a story out of my book,
says Simon.
There are pictures in it.
Let me find the story. It is my turn.

Fetch your book, Simon, says mummy,
and I will read you a story.
What story would you like?
What will it be about?
I would like a story about a tiger,
says Simon.
There is a good story about a tiger,
in my book.
Here it is.
Look at the picture of the tiger.
There is a picture of a tiger
at the front of my book.
Let me look at it, says Elizabeth.
Now listen, says mummy,
and I will read the story.